Car Logbook

CANADIAN DRIVER'S HANDBOOK

Published by The Reader's Digest Association (Canada) Ltd.
in conjunction with
the Canadian Automobile Association

FIRST EDITION
ISBN for *Canadian Driver's Handbook:* 0-88850-128-5
ISBN for *Car Logbook:* 0-88850-132-3
Printed in Canada 85 86 87 / 5 4 3 2 1

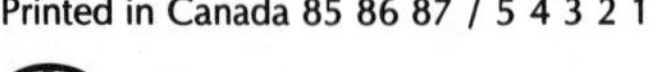

 is the trademark of the Canadian Automobile Association

CAR LOGBOOK

A lifetime diary for your car

How to use the *Car Logbook*

The charts, tables, and diagrams in this volume will enable you to keep a complete record of your car for up to ten years—the average lifetime of an automobile in Canada. From these charts you will learn how your car is performing, save money by keeping it in top shape, and spot minor problems before they become major expenses. At resale time, this book will become a valuable record of regular maintenance by a thoughtful owner.

All you have to do is fill in the blanks, starting with a record of your license, registration, insurance policy, and other important data on pages 4–5. (If you have a second car, a motorcycle, or a recreational vehicle, you can record this information on pages 6–7). Every time you fill up your tank, turn to the Fuel and Oil Costs record on pages 12–53 and mark down your odometer reading in the first column. Next, subtract the previous odometer reading to find the distance driven since your last fill-up. Write this figure in column two. In column three, note the number of litres (or U.S. gallons) of gasoline or diesel fuel it took to fill the tank. To determine your car's approximate fuel economy (in either litres per 100 kilometres or miles per gallon), flip back to the Fuel Economy Calculator on pages 8–11, and locate the consumption rate by matching the distance driven with the amount of fuel used. Enter this number, and the cost of the fill-up, in columns four and five.

Each time your car is serviced—whether by you or by a professional mechanic—record the details on the Maintenance charts provided on pages 54–63. In the event of an accident, keep calm and carefully describe the circumstances on an Accident Data Form (pp. 64–69). For quick reference, driving distances between major North American cities are listed on pages 70–71, and metric conversions appear on page 72.

4 Car Records and Data

First car

Name:

Address:

Telephone Home: Office:

Emergency telephone number:

Driver's license number:

Make, model, and year of car:

Vehicle identification number:

License plate number:

Dealer (or previous owner):

Address:

Telephone:

Date of purchase: Price paid:

Installments (if any):

Insurance policy number: Expiry date:

Insurance company and agent:

Telephone:

Keys serial number:

Tire pressure Front: Rear:

Tires rotated Spring: Fall:

Type of fuel:

Type of oil:

Other specified fluids or parts:

Name of garage:

Address:

Telephone:

CAA membership number:

Club name:

Club address:

Telephone Office: Emergency:

Social Insurance Number:

Life insurance policy number:

Insurance company and agent:

Telephone:

Passport number: Expiry date:

Credit card names and numbers:

Car contents and equipment:

Warranties:

Other information:

Second car

Name:

Address:

Telephone Home: Office:

Emergency telephone number:

Driver's license number:

Make, model, and year of car:

Vehicle identification number:

License plate number:

Dealer (or previous owner):

Address:

Telephone:

Date of purchase: Price paid:

Installments (if any):

Insurance policy number: Expiry date:

Insurance company and agent:

Telephone:

Keys serial number:

Tire pressure Front: Rear:

Tires rotated Spring: Fall:

Type of fuel:

Type of oil:

Other specified fluids or parts:

Name of garage:

Address:

Telephone:

CAA membership number:

Club name:

Club address:

Telephone Office: Emergency:

Social Insurance Number:

Life insurance policy number:

Insurance company and agent:

Telephone:

Passport number: Expiry date:

Credit card names and numbers:

Car contents and equipment:

Warranties:

Other information:

8 Fuel Economy Calculator

How to use this chart

To determine your car's fuel economy, look across the top for the figure (either litres or U.S. gallons) that approximates the amount of fuel you needed at your current fill-up. Next, look down the left-hand side to find the approximate distance driven (in kilometres or miles) since your previous fill-up. Finally, look across the line from your distance figure to the column under your litre or gallon figure. Where the row and column intersect you will find your approximate fuel consumption in litres per 100 kilometres (bold figures) or miles per U.S. gallon (light figures).

For example, let us say you have driven 328 kilometres since your last fill-up and have just refilled with 27.8 litres of gasoline. Down the left-hand side, locate the bold figure closest to the distance you have driven (330 km). Then go across this row to the column under the bold figure closest to the number of litres you have just bought (28 L). Here you will find your fuel consumption is about 8.5 litres per 100 kilometres.

If you are traveling through the United States and must fill up with U.S. gallons, you can still calculate your fuel economy simply by matching U.S. gallons (top row) with either kilometres or miles driven (side column).

Note: Because the figures have been rounded off, this chart is accurate only to within five percent.

Bold figures: Metric system (litres, kilometres, and litres per 100 kilometres)

Light figures: Imperial system (U.S. gallons, miles, and miles per U.S. gallon)

		L	GAL	**L**	GAL	**L**	GAL	**L**	GAL	**L**	GAL	**L**	GAL
Km	Mi	**10**	2.6	**12**	3.2	**14**	3.7	**16**	4.2	**18**	4.7	**20**	5.3
100	62	**10.0**	24	**12.0**	19	**14.0**	17	**16.0**	15	**18.0**	13	**20.0**	12
110	68	**9.1**	26	**10.9**	21	**12.7**	18	**14.5**	16	**16.4**	14	**18.2**	13
120	74	**8.3**	28	**10.0**	23	**11.7**	20	**13.3**	18	**15.0**	16	**16.7**	14
130	81	**7.7**	31	**9.2**	25	**10.8**	22	**12.3**	19	**13.8**	17	**15.4**	15
140	87	**7.1**	33	**8.6**	27	**10.0**	23	**11.4**	21	**12.8**	18	**14.3**	16
150	93	**6.7**	36	**8.0**	29	**9.3**	25	**10.7**	22	**12.0**	20	**13.3**	17
160	99	**6.2**	38	**7.5**	31	**8.7**	27	**10.0**	23	**11.2**	21	**12.5**	19
170	106	**5.9**	41	**7.0**	33	**8.2**	29	**9.4**	25	**10.6**	22	**11.8**	20
180	112	**5.5**	43	**6.6**	35	**7.7**	30	**8.9**	27	**10.0**	24	**11.1**	21
190	118	**5.3**	45	**6.3**	37	**7.4**	32	**8.4**	28	**9.5**	25	**10.5**	22
200	124	**5.0**	48	**6.0**	39	**7.0**	33	**8.0**	29	**9.0**	26	**10.0**	23
210	130	**4.8**	50	**5.7**	41	**6.6**	35	**7.6**	31	**8.6**	28	**9.5**	24
220	137	**4.5**	53	**5.4**	43	**6.4**	37	**7.3**	33	**8.2**	29	**9.1**	26
230	143	**4.3**	55	**5.2**	45	**6.1**	39	**6.9**	34	**7.8**	30	**8.7**	27
240	149			**5.0**	47	**5.8**	40	**6.7**	35	**7.5**	32	**8.3**	28
250	155			**4.8**	48	**5.6**	42	**6.4**	37	**7.2**	33	**8.0**	29
260	161			**4.6**	50	**5.4**	43	**6.1**	38	**6.9**	34	**7.7**	30
270	168			**4.4**	52	**5.2**	45	**5.9**	40	**6.7**	36	**7.4**	32
280	174			**4.3**	54	**5.0**	47	**5.7**	41	**6.4**	37	**7.1**	33
290	180					**4.8**	49	**5.5**	43	**6.2**	38	**6.9**	34
300	186					**4.7**	50	**5.3**	44	**6.0**	39	**6.7**	35
310	193					**4.5**	52	**5.2**	46	**5.8**	41	**6.4**	36
320	199					**4.4**	54	**5.0**	47	**5.6**	42	**6.2**	37
330	205					**4.2**	55	**4.8**	49	**5.4**	44	**6.1**	39
340	211							**4.7**	50	**5.3**	45	**5.9**	40
350	217							**4.6**	52	**5.1**	46	**5.7**	41
360	224							**4.4**	53	**5.0**	48	**5.5**	42
370	230							**4.3**	55	**4.9**	49	**5.4**	43
380	236									**4.7**	50	**5.3**	44
390	242									**4.6**	51	**5.1**	46
400	248									**4.5**	53	**5.0**	47
410	255									**4.4**	54	**4.9**	48
420	261									**4.3**	55	**4.8**	49
430	267											**4.6**	50
440	273											**4.5**	51
450	280											**4.4**	53
460	286											**4.3**	54
470	292												
480	298												
490	304												
500	311												
510	317												
520	323												
530	329												
540	335												
550	342												
560	348												
570	354												
580	360												
590	367												
600	373												
610	379												
620	385												
630	391												
640	398												
650	404												
660	410												
670	416												
680	422												
690	429												
Km	Mi	**10**	2.6	**12**	3.2	**14**	3.7	**16**	4.2	**18**	4.7	**20**	5.3
		L	GAL	**L**	GAL	**L**	GAL	**L**	GAL	**L**	GAL	**L**	GAL

L	GAL	L	GAL	L	GAL	L	GAL	L	GAL	L	GAL	L	GAL	L	GAL	L	GAL		
22	5.8	24	6.3	26	6.9	28	7.4	30	7.9	32	8.4	34	9.0	36	9.5	38	10.0	Km	Mi
																		100	62
20.0	12																	110	68
18.3	13	20.0	12															120	74
16.9	14	18.5	13	20.0	12													130	81
15.7	15	17.1	14	18.6	13	20.0	12											140	87
14.7	16	16.0	15	17.3	13	18.7	12	20.0	12									150	93
13.7	17	15.0	16	16.2	14	17.5	13	18.7	12	20.0	12							160	99
12.9	18	14.1	17	15.3	15	16.5	14	17.6	13	18.8	13	20.0	12					170	106
12.2	19	13.3	18	14.4	16	15.5	15	16.7	14	17.8	13	18.9	12	20.0	12			180	112
11.6	20	12.6	19	13.7	17	14.7	16	15.8	15	16.8	14	17.9	13	18.9	12	20.0	12	190	118
11.0	21	12.0	20	13.0	18	14.0	17	15.0	16	16.0	15	17.0	14	18.0	13	19.0	12	200	124
10.5	22	11.4	21	12.4	19	13.3	17	14.3	16	15.2	15	16.2	14	17.1	14	18.1	13	210	130
10.0	24	10.9	22	11.8	20	12.7	18	13.6	17	14.5	16	15.4	15	16.4	14	17.3	14	220	137
9.6	25	10.4	23	11.3	21	12.2	19	13.0	18	13.9	17	14.8	16	15.7	15	16.5	14	230	143
9.2	26	10.0	24	10.8	21	11.7	20	12.5	19	13.3	18	14.2	16	15.0	16	15.8	15	240	149
8.8	27	9.6	25	10.4	22	11.2	21	12.0	20	12.8	18	13.6	17	14.4	16	15.2	15	250	155
8.5	28	9.2	25	10.0	23	10.8	22	11.5	20	12.3	19	13.1	18	13.8	17	14.6	16	260	161
8.1	29	8.9	27	9.6	24	10.4	23	11.1	21	11.9	20	12.6	19	13.4	18	14.1	17	270	168
7.8	30	8.6	28	9.3	25	10.0	23	10.7	22	11.4	21	12.1	19	12.8	18	13.6	17	280	174
7.6	31	8.3	28	9.0	26	9.6	24	10.3	23	11.0	21	11.7	20	12.4	19	13.1	18	290	180
7.3	32	8.0	29	8.7	27	9.3	25	10.0	23	10.7	22	11.3	21	12.0	19	12.7	19	300	186
7.1	33	7.7	31	8.4	28	9.0	26	9.7	24	10.3	23	11.0	21	11.6	20	12.3	19	310	193
6.9	34	7.5	31	8.1	29	8.7	27	9.4	25	10.0	24	10.6	22	11.2	21	11.9	20	320	199
6.7	35	7.3	32	7.9	30	8.5	28	9.1	26	9.7	24	10.3	23	10.9	21	11.5	20	330	205
6.5	36	7.0	33	7.6	30	8.2	28	8.8	27	9.4	25	10.0	23	10.6	22	11.2	21	340	211
6.3	37	6.8	34	7.4	31	8.0	29	8.6	27	9.1	26	9.7	24	10.3	23	10.8	22	350	217
6.1	39	6.7	35	7.2	32	7.8	30	8.3	28	8.9	27	9.4	25	10.0	23	10.5	22	360	224
5.9	40	6.5	36	7.0	33	7.6	31	8.1	29	8.6	27	9.2	25	9.7	24	10.3	23	370	230
5.8	41	6.3	37	6.8	34	7.4	32	7.9	30	8.4	28	8.9	26	9.5	25	10.0	24	380	236
5.6	42	6.1	38	6.7	35	7.2	33	7.7	31	8.2	29	8.7	27	9.2	25	9.7	24	390	242
5.5	43	6.0	39	6.5	36	7.0	33	7.5	31	8.0	29	8.5	27	9.0	26	9.5	25	400	248
5.4	44	5.8	40	6.3	37	6.8	34	7.3	32	7.8	30	8.3	28	8.8	27	9.3	25	410	255
5.2	45	5.7	41	6.2	38	6.7	35	7.1	33	7.6	31	8.1	29	8.6	27	9.0	26	420	261
5.1	46	5.6	42	6.0	39	6.5	36	7.0	34	7.4	32	7.9	30	8.4	28	8.8	27	430	267
5.0	47	5.4	43	5.9	39	6.4	37	6.8	34	7.3	32	7.7	30	8.2	29	8.6	27	440	273
4.9	48	5.3	44	5.8	40	6.2	38	6.7	35	7.1	33	7.5	31	8.0	29	8.4	28	450	280
4.8	49	5.2	45	5.6	41	6.1	39	6.5	36	6.9	34	7.4	32	7.8	30	8.3	29	460	286
4.7	50	5.1	46	5.5	42	5.9	39	6.4	37	6.8	35	7.2	32	7.6	31	8.1	29	470	292
4.6	51	5.0	47	5.4	43	5.8	40	6.2	38	6.7	35	7.1	33	7.5	31	7.9	30	480	298
4.5	52	4.9	48	5.3	44	5.7	41	6.1	38	6.5	36	6.9	34	7.3	32	7.7	30	490	304
4.4	54	4.8	49	5.2	45	5.6	42	6.0	39	6.4	37	6.8	34	7.2	33	7.6	31	500	311
4.3	55	4.7	50	5.1	46	5.5	43	5.9	40	6.3	38	6.7	35	7.0	33	7.4	32	510	317
		4.6	51	5.0	47	5.4	44	5.8	41	6.1	38	6.5	36	6.9	34	7.3	32	520	323
		4.5	52	4.9	48	5.3	44	5.7	42	6.0	39	6.4	36	6.8	35	7.2	33	530	329
		4.4	53	4.8	48	5.2	45	5.5	42	5.9	40	6.3	37	6.7	35	7.0	33	540	335
		4.4	54	4.7	49	5.1	46	5.4	43	5.8	41	6.2	38	6.5	36	6.9	34	550	342
		4.3	55	4.6	50	5.0	47	5.3	44	5.7	41	6.1	39	6.4	37	6.8	35	560	348
				4.6	51	4.9	48	5.3	45	5.6	42	6.0	39	6.3	37	6.7	35	570	354
				4.5	52	4.8	49	5.2	45	5.5	43	5.9	40	6.2	38	6.5	36	580	360
				4.4	53	4.7	50	5.1	47	5.4	44	5.8	41	6.1	39	6.4	37	590	367
				4.3	54	4.7	50	5.0	47	5.3	44	5.7	41	6.0	39	6.3	37	600	373
						4.6	51	4.9	48	5.2	45	5.5	42	5.9	40	6.2	38	610	379
						4.5	52	4.8	49	5.2	46	5.5	43	5.8	40	6.1	38	620	385
						4.4	53	4.8	49	5.1	46	5.4	43	5.7	41	6.0	39	630	391
						4.4	54	4.7	50	5.0	47	5.3	44	5.6	42	5.9	40	640	398
						4.3	55	4.6	51	4.9	48	5.2	45	5.5	42	5.8	40	650	404
								4.5	52	4.8	49	5.1	45	5.4	43	5.7	41	660	410
								4.5	53	4.8	49	5.1	46	5.4	44	5.7	42	670	416
								4.4	53	4.7	50	5.0	47	5.3	44	5.6	42	680	422
								4.3	54	4.6	51	4.9	48	5.2	45	5.5	43	690	429
22	5.8	24	6.3	26	6.9	28	7.4	30	7.9	32	8.4	34	9.0	36	9.5	38	10.0	Km	Mi
L	GAL	L	GAL	L	GAL	L	GAL	L	GAL	L	GAL	L	GAL	L	GAL	L	GAL		

Km	Mi	L	GAL	L	GAL	L	GAL	L	GAL	L	GAL	L	GAL	L	GAL	L	GAL	L	GAL
		40	10.6	**42**	11.1	**44**	11.6	**46**	12.1	**48**	12.7	**50**	13.2	**52**	13.7	**54**	14.3	**56**	14.8
100	62																		
110	68																		
120	74																		
130	81																		
140	87																		
150	93																		
160	99																		
170	106																		
180	112																		
190	118																		
200	124	**20.0**	12																
210	130	**19.0**	12	**20.0**	12														
220	137	**18.2**	13	**19.1**	12	**20.0**	12												
230	143	**17.4**	13	**18.3**	13	**19.1**	12	**20.0**	12										
240	149	**16.7**	14	**17.5**	13	**18.3**	13	**19.2**	12	**20.0**	12								
250	155	**16.0**	15	**16.8**	14	**17.6**	13	**18.4**	13	**19.2**	12	**20.0**	12						
260	161	**15.4**	15	**16.1**	14	**16.9**	14	**17.7**	13	**18.5**	13	**19.2**	12	**20.0**	12				
270	168	**14.8**	16	**15.5**	15	**16.3**	14	**17.0**	14	**18.8**	13	**18.5**	13	**19.3**	12	**20.0**	12		
280	174	**14.3**	16	**15.0**	16	**15.7**	15	**16.4**	14	**17.1**	14	**17.8**	13	**18.6**	13	**19.3**	12	**20.0**	12
290	180	**13.8**	17	**14.5**	16	**15.2**	15	**15.9**	15	**16.5**	14	**17.2**	14	**17.9**	13	**18.6**	12	**19.3**	12
300	186	**13.3**	17	**14.0**	17	**14.7**	16	**15.3**	15	**16.0**	15	**16.7**	14	**17.3**	13	**18.0**	13	**18.7**	12
310	193	**12.9**	18	**13.5**	17	**14.2**	17	**14.8**	16	**15.5**	15	**16.1**	15	**16.8**	14	**17.4**	13	**18.1**	13
320	199	**12.5**	19	**13.1**	18	**13.7**	17	**14.4**	16	**15.0**	16	**15.6**	15	**16.2**	14	**16.9**	14	**17.5**	13
330	205	**12.1**	19	**12.7**	18	**13.3**	18	**13.9**	17	**14.5**	16	**15.1**	15	**15.7**	15	**16.4**	14	**17.0**	14
340	211	**11.8**	20	**12.3**	19	**12.9**	18	**13.5**	17	**14.1**	17	**14.7**	16	**15.3**	15	**15.9**	15	**16.5**	14
350	217	**11.4**	20	**12.0**	19	**12.6**	19	**13.1**	18	**13.7**	17	**14.3**	16	**14.8**	16	**15.4**	15	**16.0**	15
360	224	**11.1**	21	**11.7**	20	**12.2**	19	**12.8**	18	**13.3**	18	**13.9**	17	**14.4**	16	**15.0**	16	**15.5**	15
370	230	**10.8**	22	**11.3**	21	**11.9**	20	**12.4**	19	**13.0**	18	**13.5**	17	**14.0**	17	**14.6**	16	**15.1**	15
380	236	**10.5**	22	**11.0**	21	**11.6**	20	**12.1**	19	**12.6**	18	**13.1**	18	**13.7**	17	**14.2**	16	**14.7**	16
390	242	**10.2**	23	**10.8**	22	**11.3**	21	**11.8**	20	**12.3**	19	**12.8**	18	**13.3**	18	**13.8**	17	**14.3**	16
400	248	**10.0**	23	**10.5**	22	**11.0**	21	**11.5**	20	**12.0**	19	**12.5**	19	**13.0**	18	**13.5**	17	**14.0**	17
410	255	**9.7**	24	**10.2**	23	**10.7**	22	**11.2**	21	**11.7**	20	**12.2**	19	**12.7**	19	**13.2**	18	**13.6**	17
420	261	**9.5**	25	**10.0**	23	**10.5**	22	**10.9**	21	**11.4**	20	**11.9**	19	**12.4**	19	**12.8**	18	**13.3**	17
430	267	**9.3**	25	**9.8**	24	**10.2**	23	**10.7**	22	**11.2**	21	**11.6**	20	**12.1**	19	**12.5**	19	**13.0**	18
440	273	**9.1**	26	**9.5**	24	**10.0**	23	**10.4**	22	**10.9**	21	**11.4**	20	**11.8**	20	**12.3**	19	**12.7**	18
450	280	**8.9**	26	**9.3**	25	**9.8**	24	**10.2**	23	**10.7**	22	**11.1**	21	**11.5**	20	**12.0**	19	**12.4**	19
460	286	**8.7**	27	**9.1**	26	**9.6**	25	**10.0**	24	**10.4**	22	**10.9**	21	**11.3**	21	**11.7**	20	**12.2**	19
470	292	**8.5**	27	**8.9**	26	**9.3**	25	**9.8**	24	**10.2**	23	**10.6**	22	**11.1**	21	**11.5**	20	**11.9**	20
480	298	**8.3**	28	**8.7**	27	**9.2**	26	**9.6**	25	**10.0**	23	**10.4**	22	**10.8**	22	**11.2**	21	**11.7**	20
490	304	**8.2**	29	**8.6**	27	**9.0**	26	**9.4**	25	**9.8**	24	**10.2**	23	**10.6**	22	**11.0**	21	**11.4**	20
500	311	**8.0**	29	**8.4**	28	**8.8**	27	**9.2**	26	**9.6**	24	**10.0**	23	**10.4**	23	**10.8**	22	**11.2**	21
510	317	**7.8**	30	**8.2**	28	**8.6**	27	**9.0**	26	**9.4**	25	**9.8**	24	**10.2**	23	**10.6**	22	**11.0**	21
520	323	**7.7**	30	**8.1**	29	**8.5**	28	**8.8**	27	**9.2**	25	**9.6**	24	**10.0**	23	**10.4**	22	**10.8**	22
530	329	**7.5**	31	**7.9**	30	**8.3**	28	**8.7**	27	**9.0**	26	**9.4**	25	**9.8**	24	**10.2**	23	**10.6**	22
540	335	**7.4**	32	**7.8**	30	**8.1**	29	**8.5**	28	**8.9**	26	**9.2**	25	**9.6**	24	**10.0**	23	**10.4**	23
550	342	**7.3**	32	**7.6**	31	**8.0**	29	**8.4**	28	**8.7**	27	**9.1**	26	**9.4**	25	**9.8**	24	**10.2**	23
560	348	**7.1**	33	**7.5**	31	**7.8**	30	**8.2**	29	**8.6**	27	**8.9**	26	**9.3**	25	**9.6**	24	**10.0**	23
570	354	**7.0**	33	**7.4**	32	**7.7**	30	**8.1**	29	**8.4**	28	**8.8**	27	**9.1**	26	**9.5**	25	**9.8**	24
580	360	**6.9**	34	**7.2**	32	**7.6**	31	**7.9**	30	**8.3**	28	**8.6**	27	**9.0**	26	**9.3**	25	**9.6**	24
590	367	**6.8**	35	**7.1**	33	**7.4**	32	**7.8**	30	**8.1**	29	**8.5**	28	**8.8**	27	**9.1**	26	**9.5**	25
600	373	**6.7**	35	**7.0**	34	**7.3**	32	**7.7**	31	**8.0**	29	**8.3**	28	**8.7**	27	**9.0**	26	**9.3**	25
610	379	**6.5**	36	**6.9**	34	**7.2**	33	**7.5**	31	**7.9**	30	**8.2**	29	**8.5**	28	**8.8**	26	**9.2**	26
620	385	**6.4**	36	**6.8**	35	**7.1**	33	**7.4**	32	**7.7**	30	**8.1**	29	**8.4**	28	**8.7**	27	**9.0**	26
630	391	**6.3**	37	**6.7**	35	**7.0**	34	**7.3**	32	**7.6**	31	**7.9**	30	**8.2**	28	**8.6**	27	**8.9**	26
640	398	**6.2**	37	**6.6**	36	**6.9**	34	**7.2**	33	**7.5**	31	**7.8**	30	**8.1**	29	**8.4**	28	**8.7**	27
650	404	**6.1**	38	**6.5**	36	**6.8**	35	**7.1**	33	**7.4**	32	**7.7**	31	**8.0**	29	**8.3**	28	**8.6**	27
660	410	**6.1**	39	**6.4**	37	**6.7**	35	**7.0**	34	**7.3**	32	**7.6**	31	**7.9**	30	**8.2**	29	**8.5**	28
670	416	**6.0**	39	**6.3**	37	**6.6**	36	**6.9**	34	**7.2**	33	**7.5**	31	**7.8**	30	**8.0**	29	**8.3**	28
680	422	**5.9**	40	**6.2**	38	**6.5**	36	**6.8**	35	**7.0**	33	**7.3**	32	**7.6**	31	**7.9**	29	**8.2**	28
690	429	**5.8**	40	**6.1**	39	**6.4**	37	**6.7**	35	**6.9**	34	**7.2**	32	**7.5**	31	**7.8**	30	**8.1**	29
Km	Mi	**40**	10.6	**42**	11.1	**44**	11.6	**46**	12.1	**48**	12.7	**50**	13.2	**52**	13.7	**54**	14.3	**56**	14.8
		L	GAL	L	GAL	L	GAL	L	GAL	L	GAL	L	GAL	L	GAL	L	GAL	L	GAL

L	GAL	L	GAL	L	GAL	L	GAL	L	GAL	L	GAL		
58	15.3	60	15.8	62	16.4	64	16.9	66	17.4	68	18	Km	Mi
												100	62
												110	68
												120	74
												130	81
												140	87
												150	93
												160	99
												170	106
												180	112
												190	118
												200	124
												210	130
												220	137
												230	143
												240	149
												250	155
												260	161
												270	168
												280	174
20.0	12											290	180
19.3	12	20.0	12									300	186
18.7	13	19.3	12	20.0	12							310	193
18.1	13	18.7	12	19.4	12	20.0	12					320	199
17.6	13	18.2	13	18.8	12	19.4	12	20.0	12			330	205
17.0	14	17.6	13	18.2	13	18.8	12	19.4	12	20.0	12	340	211
16.6	14	17.1	14	17.7	13	18.3	13	18.8	12	19.4	12	350	217
16.1	15	16.7	14	17.2	14	17.8	13	18.3	13	18.9	12	360	224
15.7	15	16.2	14	16.7	14	17.3	14	17.8	13	18.4	13	370	230
15.3	15	15.8	15	16.3	14	16.8	14	17.4	13	17.9	13	380	236
14.9	16	15.4	15	15.9	15	16.4	14	16.9	14	17.4	13	390	242
14.5	16	15.0	16	15.5	15	16.0	15	16.5	14	17.0	14	400	248
14.1	17	14.6	16	15.1	15	15.6	15	16.1	15	16.6	14	410	255
13.8	17	14.3	16	14.8	16	15.2	15	15.7	15	16.2	14	420	261
13.5	17	13.9	17	14.4	16	14.9	16	15.3	15	15.8	15	430	267
13.2	18	13.6	17	14.1	17	14.5	16	15.0	16	15.4	15	440	273
12.9	18	13.3	18	13.8	17	14.2	16	14.7	16	15.1	15	450	280
12.6	18	13.0	18	13.5	17	13.9	17	14.3	16	14.8	16	460	286
12.3	19	12.8	18	13.2	18	13.6	17	14.0	17	14.5	16	470	292
12.1	19	12.5	19	12.9	18	13.3	18	13.7	17	14.2	16	480	298
11.8	20	12.2	19	12.6	18	13.1	18	13.5	17	13.9	17	490	304
11.6	20	12.0	20	12.4	19	12.8	18	13.2	18	13.6	17	500	311
11.4	21	11.8	20	12.1	19	12.5	19	12.9	18	13.3	18	510	317
11.1	21	11.5	20	11.9	19	12.3	19	12.7	18	13.1	18	520	323
10.9	21	11.3	21	11.7	20	12.1	19	12.4	19	12.8	18	530	329
10.7	22	11.1	21	11.5	20	11.8	20	12.2	19	12.6	19	540	335
10.5	22	10.9	22	11.3	21	11.6	20	12.0	20	12.4	19	550	342
10.3	23	10.7	22	11.1	21	11.4	21	11.8	20	12.1	19	560	348
10.2	23	10.5	22	10.9	21	11.2	21	11.6	20	11.9	20	570	354
10.0	23	10.3	23	10.7	22	11.0	21	11.4	21	11.7	20	580	360
9.8	24	10.2	23	10.5	22	10.8	22	11.2	21	11.5	20	590	367
9.7	24	10.0	24	10.3	23	10.7	22	11.0	21	11.3	21	600	373
9.5	25	9.8	24	10.2	23	10.5	22	10.8	22	11.1	21	610	379
9.3	25	9.7	24	10.0	23	10.3	23	10.6	22	11.0	21	620	385
9.2	25	9.5	25	9.8	24	10.1	23	10.5	22	10.8	22	630	391
9.1	26	9.4	25	9.7	24	10.0	23	10.3	23	10.6	22	640	398
8.9	26	9.2	25	9.5	25	9.8	24	10.1	23	10.5	22	650	404
8.8	27	9.1	26	9.4	25	9.7	24	10.0	23	10.3	23	660	410
8.6	27	8.9	26	9.2	25	9.5	25	9.8	24	10.1	23	670	416
8.5	27	8.8	27	9.1	26	9.4	25	9.7	24	10.0	23	680	422
8.4	28	8.7	27	9.0	26	9.3	25	9.6	25	9.8	24	690	429
58	15.3	60	15.8	62	16.4	64	16.9	66	17.4	68	18	Km	Mi
L	GAL	L	GAL	L	GAL	L	GAL	L	GAL	L	GAL		

U.S. and Canadian gallons
To add to the problem of converting metric and imperial measures is the fact that the little-used Canadian gallon is 20 percent larger than the U.S. gallon. Use the table below to convert between these two measures.

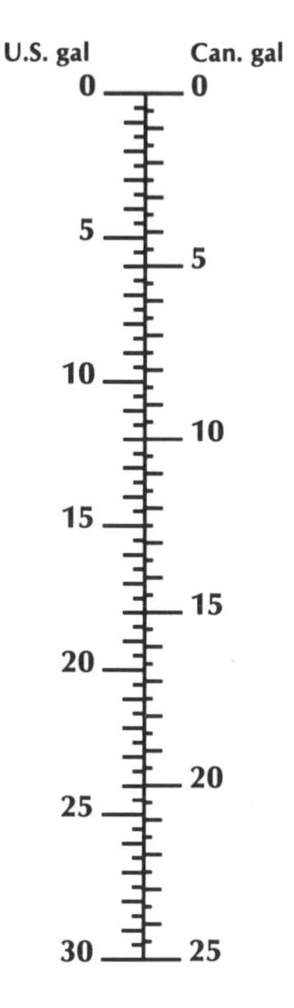

Fuel and Oil Costs

FUEL COSTS

	RECORD ODOMETER READING	SUBTRACT PREVIOUS READING (Enter Result)	RECORD NUMBER OF LITRES	CALCULATE FUEL ECONOMY (SEE PP. 8–11)	RECORD FILL-UP COST	
MONTH OF:						
MONTH OF:						
MONTH OF:						
	GASOLINE COSTS FOR THREE MONTHS					

OIL COSTS

RECORD ODOMETER READING	SUBTRACT PREVIOUS READING (Enter Result)	RECORD NUMBER OF LITRES	DATE	RECORD OIL COST	
OIL COSTS FOR THREE MONTHS					

FUEL COSTS

	RECORD ODOMETER READING	SUBTRACT PREVIOUS READING (Enter Result)	RECORD NUMBER OF LITRES	CALCULATE FUEL ECONOMY (SEE PP. 8–11)	RECORD FILL-UP COST	
MONTH OF:						
MONTH OF:						
MONTH OF:						
	GASOLINE COSTS FOR THREE MONTHS					

OIL COSTS

RECORD ODOMETER READING	SUBTRACT PREVIOUS READING (Enter Result)	RECORD NUMBER OF LITRES	DATE	RECORD OIL COST	
OIL COSTS FOR THREE MONTHS					

Fuel and Oil Costs

FUEL COSTS

	RECORD ODOMETER READING	SUBTRACT PREVIOUS READING (Enter Result)	RECORD NUMBER OF LITRES	CALCULATE FUEL ECONOMY (SEE PP. 8–11)	RECORD FILL-UP COST	
MONTH OF:						
MONTH OF:						
MONTH OF:						
	GASOLINE COSTS FOR THREE MONTHS					

OIL COSTS

RECORD ODOMETER READING	SUBTRACT PREVIOUS READING (Enter Result)	RECORD NUMBER OF LITRES	DATE	RECORD OIL COST	
OIL COSTS FOR THREE MONTHS					

FUEL COSTS

	RECORD ODOMETER READING	SUBTRACT PREVIOUS READING (Enter Result)	RECORD NUMBER OF LITRES	CALCULATE FUEL ECONOMY (SEE PP. 8–11)	RECORD FILL-UP COST	
MONTH OF:						
MONTH OF:						
MONTH OF:						
	GASOLINE COSTS FOR THREE MONTHS					

OIL COSTS

RECORD ODOMETER READING	SUBTRACT PREVIOUS READING (Enter Result)	RECORD NUMBER OF LITRES	DATE	RECORD OIL COST	
OIL COSTS FOR THREE MONTHS					

Fuel and Oil Costs

FUEL COSTS

	RECORD ODOMETER READING	SUBTRACT PREVIOUS READING (Enter Result)	RECORD NUMBER OF LITRES	CALCULATE FUEL ECONOMY (SEE PP. 8–11)	RECORD FILL-UP COST	
MONTH OF:						
MONTH OF:						
MONTH OF:						
	GASOLINE COSTS FOR THREE MONTHS					

OIL COSTS

RECORD ODOMETER READING	SUBTRACT PREVIOUS READING (Enter Result)	RECORD NUMBER OF LITRES	DATE	RECORD OIL COST	
OIL COSTS FOR THREE MONTHS					

FUEL COSTS

	RECORD ODOMETER READING	SUBTRACT PREVIOUS READING (Enter Result)	RECORD NUMBER OF LITRES	CALCULATE FUEL ECONOMY (SEE PP. 8–11)	RECORD FILL-UP COST	
MONTH OF:						
MONTH OF:						
MONTH OF:						
				GASOLINE COSTS FOR THREE MONTHS		

OIL COSTS

RECORD ODOMETER READING	SUBTRACT PREVIOUS READING (Enter Result)	RECORD NUMBER OF LITRES	DATE	RECORD OIL COST	
			OIL COSTS FOR THREE MONTHS		

Fuel and Oil Costs

FUEL COSTS

	RECORD ODOMETER READING	SUBTRACT PREVIOUS READING (Enter Result)	RECORD NUMBER OF LITRES	CALCULATE FUEL ECONOMY (SEE PP. 8–11)	RECORD FILL-UP COST	
MONTH OF:						
MONTH OF:						
MONTH OF:						
	GASOLINE COSTS FOR THREE MONTHS					

OIL COSTS

RECORD ODOMETER READING	SUBTRACT PREVIOUS READING (Enter Result)	RECORD NUMBER OF LITRES	DATE	RECORD OIL COST	
OIL COSTS FOR THREE MONTHS					

FUEL COSTS

	RECORD ODOMETER READING	SUBTRACT PREVIOUS READING (Enter Result)	RECORD NUMBER OF LITRES	CALCULATE FUEL ECONOMY (SEE PP. 8–11)	RECORD FILL-UP COST	
MONTH OF:						
MONTH OF:						
MONTH OF:						
	GASOLINE COSTS FOR THREE MONTHS					

OIL COSTS

RECORD ODOMETER READING	SUBTRACT PREVIOUS READING (Enter Result)	RECORD NUMBER OF LITRES	DATE	RECORD OIL COST	
OIL COSTS FOR THREE MONTHS					

Fuel and Oil Costs

FUEL COSTS

	RECORD ODOMETER READING	SUBTRACT PREVIOUS READING (Enter Result)	RECORD NUMBER OF LITRES	CALCULATE FUEL ECONOMY (SEE PP. 8–11)	RECORD FILL-UP COST	
MONTH OF:						
MONTH OF:						
MONTH OF:						
	GASOLINE COSTS FOR THREE MONTHS					

OIL COSTS

RECORD ODOMETER READING	SUBTRACT PREVIOUS READING (Enter Result)	RECORD NUMBER OF LITRES	DATE	RECORD OIL COST	
OIL COSTS FOR THREE MONTHS					

FUEL COSTS

	RECORD ODOMETER READING	SUBTRACT PREVIOUS READING (Enter Result)	RECORD NUMBER OF LITRES	CALCULATE FUEL ECONOMY (SEE PP. 8–11)	RECORD FILL-UP COST	
MONTH OF:						
MONTH OF:						
MONTH OF:						
	GASOLINE COSTS FOR THREE MONTHS					

OIL COSTS

RECORD ODOMETER READING	SUBTRACT PREVIOUS READING (Enter Result)	RECORD NUMBER OF LITRES	DATE	RECORD OIL COST	
OIL COSTS FOR THREE MONTHS					

FUEL COSTS

	RECORD ODOMETER READING	SUBTRACT PREVIOUS READING (Enter Result)	RECORD NUMBER OF LITRES	CALCULATE FUEL ECONOMY (SEE PP. 8–11)	RECORD FILL-UP COST	
MONTH OF:						
MONTH OF:						
MONTH OF:						
	GASOLINE COSTS FOR THREE MONTHS					

OIL COSTS

RECORD ODOMETER READING	SUBTRACT PREVIOUS READING (Enter Result)	RECORD NUMBER OF LITRES	DATE	RECORD OIL COST	
OIL COSTS FOR THREE MONTHS					

FUEL COSTS

	RECORD ODOMETER READING	SUBTRACT PREVIOUS READING (Enter Result)	RECORD NUMBER OF LITRES	CALCULATE FUEL ECONOMY (SEE PP. 8–11)	RECORD FILL-UP COST	
MONTH OF:						
MONTH OF:						
MONTH OF:						
				GASOLINE COSTS FOR THREE MONTHS		

OIL COSTS

RECORD ODOMETER READING	SUBTRACT PREVIOUS READING (Enter Result)	RECORD NUMBER OF LITRES	DATE	RECORD OIL COST	
			OIL COSTS FOR THREE MONTHS		

Fuel and Oil Costs

FUEL COSTS

	RECORD ODOMETER READING	SUBTRACT PREVIOUS READING (Enter Result)	RECORD NUMBER OF LITRES	CALCULATE FUEL ECONOMY (SEE PP. 8–11)	RECORD FILL-UP COST	
MONTH OF:						
MONTH OF:						
MONTH OF:						
				GASOLINE COSTS FOR THREE MONTHS		

OIL COSTS

RECORD ODOMETER READING	SUBTRACT PREVIOUS READING (Enter Result)	RECORD NUMBER OF LITRES	DATE	RECORD OIL COST	
			OIL COSTS FOR THREE MONTHS		

FUEL COSTS

	RECORD ODOMETER READING	SUBTRACT PREVIOUS READING (Enter Result)	RECORD NUMBER OF LITRES	CALCULATE FUEL ECONOMY (SEE PP. 8–11)	RECORD FILL-UP COST	
MONTH OF:						
MONTH OF:						
MONTH OF:						
				GASOLINE COSTS FOR THREE MONTHS		

OIL COSTS

RECORD ODOMETER READING	SUBTRACT PREVIOUS READING (Enter Result)	RECORD NUMBER OF LITRES	DATE	RECORD OIL COST	
			OIL COSTS FOR THREE MONTHS		

Fuel and Oil Costs

FUEL COSTS

	RECORD ODOMETER READING	SUBTRACT PREVIOUS READING (Enter Result)	RECORD NUMBER OF LITRES	CALCULATE FUEL ECONOMY (SEE PP. 8–11)	RECORD FILL-UP COST	
MONTH OF:						
MONTH OF:						
MONTH OF:						
	GASOLINE COSTS FOR THREE MONTHS					

OIL COSTS

RECORD ODOMETER READING	SUBTRACT PREVIOUS READING (Enter Result)	RECORD NUMBER OF LITRES	DATE	RECORD OIL COST	
OIL COSTS FOR THREE MONTHS					

FUEL COSTS

	RECORD ODOMETER READING	SUBTRACT PREVIOUS READING (Enter Result)	RECORD NUMBER OF LITRES	CALCULATE FUEL ECONOMY (SEE PP. 8–11)	RECORD FILL-UP COST	
MONTH OF:						
MONTH OF:						
MONTH OF:						
	GASOLINE COSTS FOR THREE MONTHS					

OIL COSTS

RECORD ODOMETER READING	SUBTRACT PREVIOUS READING (Enter Result)	RECORD NUMBER OF LITRES	DATE	RECORD OIL COST	
OIL COSTS FOR THREE MONTHS					

Fuel and Oil Costs

FUEL COSTS

	RECORD ODOMETER READING	SUBTRACT PREVIOUS READING (Enter Result)	RECORD NUMBER OF LITRES	CALCULATE FUEL ECONOMY (SEE PP. 8–11)	RECORD FILL-UP COST	
MONTH OF:						
MONTH OF:						
MONTH OF:						
	GASOLINE COSTS FOR THREE MONTHS					

OIL COSTS

RECORD ODOMETER READING	SUBTRACT PREVIOUS READING (Enter Result)	RECORD NUMBER OF LITRES	DATE	RECORD OIL COST	
OIL COSTS FOR THREE MONTHS					

FUEL COSTS

	RECORD ODOMETER READING	SUBTRACT PREVIOUS READING (Enter Result)	RECORD NUMBER OF LITRES	CALCULATE FUEL ECONOMY (SEE PP. 8–11)	RECORD FILL-UP COST	
MONTH OF:						
MONTH OF:						
MONTH OF:						
	GASOLINE COSTS FOR THREE MONTHS					

OIL COSTS

RECORD ODOMETER READING	SUBTRACT PREVIOUS READING (Enter Result)	RECORD NUMBER OF LITRES	DATE	RECORD OIL COST	
OIL COSTS FOR THREE MONTHS					

Fuel and Oil Costs

FUEL COSTS

	RECORD ODOMETER READING	SUBTRACT PREVIOUS READING (Enter Result)	RECORD NUMBER OF LITRES	CALCULATE FUEL ECONOMY (SEE PP. 8–11)	RECORD FILL-UP COST	
MONTH OF:						
MONTH OF:						
MONTH OF:						
	GASOLINE COSTS FOR THREE MONTHS					

OIL COSTS

RECORD ODOMETER READING	SUBTRACT PREVIOUS READING (Enter Result)	RECORD NUMBER OF LITRES	DATE	RECORD OIL COST	
OIL COSTS FOR THREE MONTHS					

FUEL COSTS

	RECORD ODOMETER READING	SUBTRACT PREVIOUS READING (Enter Result)	RECORD NUMBER OF LITRES	CALCULATE FUEL ECONOMY (SEE PP. 8–11)	RECORD FILL-UP COST	
MONTH OF:						
MONTH OF:						
MONTH OF:						
				GASOLINE COSTS FOR THREE MONTHS		

OIL COSTS

RECORD ODOMETER READING	SUBTRACT PREVIOUS READING (Enter Result)	RECORD NUMBER OF LITRES	DATE	RECORD OIL COST	
			OIL COSTS FOR THREE MONTHS		

Fuel and Oil Costs

FUEL COSTS

	RECORD ODOMETER READING	SUBTRACT PREVIOUS READING (Enter Result)	RECORD NUMBER OF LITRES	CALCULATE FUEL ECONOMY (SEE PP. 8–11)	RECORD FILL-UP COST	
MONTH OF:						
MONTH OF:						
MONTH OF:						
	GASOLINE COSTS FOR THREE MONTHS					

OIL COSTS

RECORD ODOMETER READING	SUBTRACT PREVIOUS READING (Enter Result)	RECORD NUMBER OF LITRES	DATE	RECORD OIL COST	
OIL COSTS FOR THREE MONTHS					

FUEL COSTS

	RECORD ODOMETER READING	SUBTRACT PREVIOUS READING (Enter Result)	RECORD NUMBER OF LITRES	CALCULATE FUEL ECONOMY (SEE PP. 8–11)	RECORD FILL-UP COST	
MONTH OF:						
MONTH OF:						
MONTH OF:						
				GASOLINE COSTS FOR THREE MONTHS		

OIL COSTS

RECORD ODOMETER READING	SUBTRACT PREVIOUS READING (Enter Result)	RECORD NUMBER OF LITRES	DATE	RECORD OIL COST	
			OIL COSTS FOR THREE MONTHS		

Fuel and Oil Costs

FUEL COSTS

	RECORD ODOMETER READING	SUBTRACT PREVIOUS READING (Enter Result)	RECORD NUMBER OF LITRES	CALCULATE FUEL ECONOMY (SEE PP. 8–11)	RECORD FILL-UP COST	
MONTH OF:						
MONTH OF:						
MONTH OF:						
	GASOLINE COSTS FOR THREE MONTHS					

OIL COSTS

RECORD ODOMETER READING	SUBTRACT PREVIOUS READING (Enter Result)	RECORD NUMBER OF LITRES	DATE	RECORD OIL COST	
OIL COSTS FOR THREE MONTHS					

FUEL COSTS

	RECORD ODOMETER READING	SUBTRACT PREVIOUS READING (Enter Result)	RECORD NUMBER OF LITRES	CALCULATE FUEL ECONOMY (SEE PP. 8–11)	RECORD FILL-UP COST	
MONTH OF:						
MONTH OF:						
MONTH OF:						
				GASOLINE COSTS FOR THREE MONTHS		

OIL COSTS

RECORD ODOMETER READING	SUBTRACT PREVIOUS READING (Enter Result)	RECORD NUMBER OF LITRES	DATE	RECORD OIL COST	
			OIL COSTS FOR THREE MONTHS		

Fuel and Oil Costs

FUEL COSTS

	RECORD ODOMETER READING	SUBTRACT PREVIOUS READING (Enter Result)	RECORD NUMBER OF LITRES	CALCULATE FUEL ECONOMY (SEE PP. 8–11)	RECORD FILL-UP COST	
MONTH OF:						
MONTH OF:						
MONTH OF:						
	GASOLINE COSTS FOR THREE MONTHS					

OIL COSTS

RECORD ODOMETER READING	SUBTRACT PREVIOUS READING (Enter Result)	RECORD NUMBER OF LITRES	DATE	RECORD OIL COST	
OIL COSTS FOR THREE MONTHS					

FUEL COSTS

	RECORD ODOMETER READING	SUBTRACT PREVIOUS READING (Enter Result)	RECORD NUMBER OF LITRES	CALCULATE FUEL ECONOMY (SEE PP. 8–11)	RECORD FILL-UP COST	
MONTH OF:						
MONTH OF:						
MONTH OF:						
	GASOLINE COSTS FOR THREE MONTHS					

OIL COSTS

RECORD ODOMETER READING	SUBTRACT PREVIOUS READING (Enter Result)	RECORD NUMBER OF LITRES	DATE	RECORD OIL COST	
OIL COSTS FOR THREE MONTHS					

Fuel and Oil Costs

FUEL COSTS

	RECORD ODOMETER READING	SUBTRACT PREVIOUS READING (Enter Result)	RECORD NUMBER OF LITRES	CALCULATE FUEL ECONOMY (SEE PP. 8–11)	RECORD FILL-UP COST	
MONTH OF:						
MONTH OF:						
MONTH OF:						
	GASOLINE COSTS FOR THREE MONTHS					

OIL COSTS

RECORD ODOMETER READING	SUBTRACT PREVIOUS READING (Enter Result)	RECORD NUMBER OF LITRES	DATE	RECORD OIL COST	
OIL COSTS FOR THREE MONTHS					

FUEL COSTS

	RECORD ODOMETER READING	SUBTRACT PREVIOUS READING (Enter Result)	RECORD NUMBER OF LITRES	CALCULATE FUEL ECONOMY (SEE PP. 8–11)	RECORD FILL-UP COST	
MONTH OF:						
MONTH OF:						
MONTH OF:						
	GASOLINE COSTS FOR THREE MONTHS					

OIL COSTS

RECORD ODOMETER READING	SUBTRACT PREVIOUS READING (Enter Result)	RECORD NUMBER OF LITRES	DATE	RECORD OIL COST	
OIL COSTS FOR THREE MONTHS					

Fuel and Oil Costs

FUEL COSTS

	RECORD ODOMETER READING	SUBTRACT PREVIOUS READING (Enter Result)	RECORD NUMBER OF LITRES	CALCULATE FUEL ECONOMY (SEE PP. 8–11)	RECORD FILL-UP COST	
MONTH OF:						
MONTH OF:						
MONTH OF:						
	GASOLINE COSTS FOR THREE MONTHS					

OIL COSTS

RECORD ODOMETER READING	SUBTRACT PREVIOUS READING (Enter Result)	RECORD NUMBER OF LITRES	DATE	RECORD OIL COST	
OIL COSTS FOR THREE MONTHS					

FUEL COSTS

	RECORD ODOMETER READING	SUBTRACT PREVIOUS READING (Enter Result)	RECORD NUMBER OF LITRES	CALCULATE FUEL ECONOMY (SEE PP. 8–11)	RECORD FILL-UP COST	
MONTH OF:						
MONTH OF:						
MONTH OF:						
	GASOLINE COSTS FOR THREE MONTHS					

OIL COSTS

RECORD ODOMETER READING	SUBTRACT PREVIOUS READING (Enter Result)	RECORD NUMBER OF LITRES	DATE	RECORD OIL COST	
OIL COSTS FOR THREE MONTHS					

Fuel and Oil Costs

FUEL COSTS

	RECORD ODOMETER READING	SUBTRACT PREVIOUS READING (Enter Result)	RECORD NUMBER OF LITRES	CALCULATE FUEL ECONOMY (SEE PP. 8–11)	RECORD FILL-UP COST	
MONTH OF:						
MONTH OF:						
MONTH OF:						
	GASOLINE COSTS FOR THREE MONTHS					

OIL COSTS

RECORD ODOMETER READING	SUBTRACT PREVIOUS READING (Enter Result)	RECORD NUMBER OF LITRES	DATE	RECORD OIL COST	
OIL COSTS FOR THREE MONTHS					

FUEL COSTS

	RECORD ODOMETER READING	SUBTRACT PREVIOUS READING (Enter Result)	RECORD NUMBER OF LITRES	CALCULATE FUEL ECONOMY (SEE PP. 8–11)	RECORD FILL-UP COST	
MONTH OF:						
MONTH OF:						
MONTH OF:						
	GASOLINE COSTS FOR THREE MONTHS					

OIL COSTS

RECORD ODOMETER READING	SUBTRACT PREVIOUS READING (Enter Result)	RECORD NUMBER OF LITRES	DATE	RECORD OIL COST	
OIL COSTS FOR THREE MONTHS					

Fuel and Oil Costs

FUEL COSTS

	RECORD ODOMETER READING	SUBTRACT PREVIOUS READING (Enter Result)	RECORD NUMBER OF LITRES	CALCULATE FUEL ECONOMY (SEE PP. 8–11)	RECORD FILL-UP COST	
MONTH OF:						
MONTH OF:						
MONTH OF:						
				GASOLINE COSTS FOR THREE MONTHS		

OIL COSTS

RECORD ODOMETER READING	SUBTRACT PREVIOUS READING (Enter Result)	RECORD NUMBER OF LITRES	DATE	RECORD OIL COST	
			OIL COSTS FOR THREE MONTHS		

FUEL COSTS

	RECORD ODOMETER READING	SUBTRACT PREVIOUS READING (Enter Result)	RECORD NUMBER OF LITRES	CALCULATE FUEL ECONOMY (SEE PP. 8–11)	RECORD FILL-UP COST	
MONTH OF:						
MONTH OF:						
MONTH OF:						
	GASOLINE COSTS FOR THREE MONTHS					

OIL COSTS

RECORD ODOMETER READING	SUBTRACT PREVIOUS READING (Enter Result)	RECORD NUMBER OF LITRES	DATE	RECORD OIL COST	
OIL COSTS FOR THREE MONTHS					

Fuel and Oil Costs

FUEL COSTS

	RECORD ODOMETER READING	SUBTRACT PREVIOUS READING (Enter Result)	RECORD NUMBER OF LITRES	CALCULATE FUEL ECONOMY (SEE PP. 8–11)	RECORD FILL-UP COST	
MONTH OF:						
MONTH OF:						
MONTH OF:						
	GASOLINE COSTS FOR THREE MONTHS					

OIL COSTS

RECORD ODOMETER READING	SUBTRACT PREVIOUS READING (Enter Result)	RECORD NUMBER OF LITRES	DATE	RECORD OIL COST	
OIL COSTS FOR THREE MONTHS					

FUEL COSTS

	RECORD ODOMETER READING	SUBTRACT PREVIOUS READING (Enter Result)	RECORD NUMBER OF LITRES	CALCULATE FUEL ECONOMY (SEE PP. 8–11)	RECORD FILL-UP COST	
MONTH OF:						
MONTH OF:						
MONTH OF:						
	GASOLINE COSTS FOR THREE MONTHS					

OIL COSTS

RECORD ODOMETER READING	SUBTRACT PREVIOUS READING (Enter Result)	RECORD NUMBER OF LITRES	DATE	RECORD OIL COST	
OIL COSTS FOR THREE MONTHS					

Fuel and Oil Costs

FUEL COSTS

	RECORD ODOMETER READING	SUBTRACT PREVIOUS READING (Enter Result)	RECORD NUMBER OF LITRES	CALCULATE FUEL ECONOMY (SEE PP. 8–11)	RECORD FILL-UP COST	
MONTH OF:						
MONTH OF:						
MONTH OF:						
				GASOLINE COSTS FOR THREE MONTHS		

OIL COSTS

RECORD ODOMETER READING	SUBTRACT PREVIOUS READING (Enter Result)	RECORD NUMBER OF LITRES	DATE	RECORD OIL COST	
			OIL COSTS FOR THREE MONTHS		

FUEL COSTS

	RECORD ODOMETER READING	SUBTRACT PREVIOUS READING (Enter Result)	RECORD NUMBER OF LITRES	CALCULATE FUEL ECONOMY (SEE PP. 8–11)	RECORD FILL-UP COST	
MONTH OF:						
MONTH OF:						
MONTH OF:						
				GASOLINE COSTS FOR THREE MONTHS		

OIL COSTS

RECORD ODOMETER READING	SUBTRACT PREVIOUS READING (Enter Result)	RECORD NUMBER OF LITRES	DATE	RECORD OIL COST	
			OIL COSTS FOR THREE MONTHS		

Fuel and Oil Costs

FUEL COSTS

	RECORD ODOMETER READING	SUBTRACT PREVIOUS READING (Enter Result)	RECORD NUMBER OF LITRES	CALCULATE FUEL ECONOMY (SEE PP. 8–11)	RECORD FILL-UP COST	
MONTH OF:						
MONTH OF:						
MONTH OF:						
	GASOLINE COSTS FOR THREE MONTHS					

OIL COSTS

RECORD ODOMETER READING	SUBTRACT PREVIOUS READING (Enter Result)	RECORD NUMBER OF LITRES	DATE	RECORD OIL COST	
OIL COSTS FOR THREE MONTHS					

FUEL COSTS

	RECORD ODOMETER READING	SUBTRACT PREVIOUS READING (Enter Result)	RECORD NUMBER OF LITRES	CALCULATE FUEL ECONOMY (SEE PP. 8–11)	RECORD FILL-UP COST	
MONTH OF:						
MONTH OF:						
MONTH OF:						
				GASOLINE COSTS FOR THREE MONTHS		

OIL COSTS

RECORD ODOMETER READING	SUBTRACT PREVIOUS READING (Enter Result)	RECORD NUMBER OF LITRES	DATE	RECORD OIL COST	
			OIL COSTS FOR THREE MONTHS		

Fuel and Oil Costs

FUEL COSTS

	RECORD ODOMETER READING	SUBTRACT PREVIOUS READING (Enter Result)	RECORD NUMBER OF LITRES	CALCULATE FUEL ECONOMY (SEE PP. 8–11)	RECORD FILL-UP COST	
MONTH OF:						
MONTH OF:						
MONTH OF:						
					GASOLINE COSTS FOR THREE MONTHS		

OIL COSTS

RECORD ODOMETER READING	SUBTRACT PREVIOUS READING (Enter Result)	RECORD NUMBER OF LITRES	DATE	RECORD OIL COST	
			OIL COSTS FOR THREE MONTHS		

FUEL COSTS

	RECORD ODOMETER READING	SUBTRACT PREVIOUS READING (Enter Result)	RECORD NUMBER OF LITRES	CALCULATE FUEL ECONOMY (SEE PP. 8–11)	RECORD FILL-UP COST	
MONTH OF:						
MONTH OF:						
MONTH OF:						
				GASOLINE COSTS FOR THREE MONTHS		

OIL COSTS

RECORD ODOMETER READING	SUBTRACT PREVIOUS READING (Enter Result)	RECORD NUMBER OF LITRES	DATE	RECORD OIL COST	
			OIL COSTS FOR THREE MONTHS		

Maintenance Record

REPAIR COSTS 19____

DATE	ODOMETER READING	RECORD THE TYPE OF WORK PERFORMED ON YOUR CAR	TOTAL COST	
		ANNUAL REPAIR COST		

MAINTENANCE COSTS 19____

DATE	ODOMETER READING	RECORD THE TYPE OF WORK PERFORMED ON YOUR CAR	TOTAL COST	
		TIRES ROTATED (SPRING)		
		SPRING TUNE-UP AND OIL CHANGE		
		TIRES ROTATED (FALL)		
		FALL TUNE-UP AND OIL CHANGE		
		INSPECT BRAKES		
		INSPECT STEERING AND SUSPENSION		
		LUBRICATE CHASSIS		
		REPLACE COOLANT		
		CHECK FLUID LEVELS		
		ANNUAL MAINTENANCE COST		

REPAIR COSTS 19____

DATE	ODOMETER READING	RECORD THE TYPE OF WORK PERFORMED ON YOUR CAR	TOTAL COST	
		ANNUAL REPAIR COST		

MAINTENANCE COSTS 19____

DATE	ODOMETER READING	RECORD THE TYPE OF WORK PERFORMED ON YOUR CAR	TOTAL COST	
		TIRES ROTATED (SPRING)		
		SPRING TUNE-UP AND OIL CHANGE		
		TIRES ROTATED (FALL)		
		FALL TUNE-UP AND OIL CHANGE		
		INSPECT BRAKES		
		INSPECT STEERING AND SUSPENSION		
		LUBRICATE CHASSIS		
		REPLACE COOLANT		
		CHECK FLUID LEVELS		
		ANNUAL MAINTENANCE COST		

REPAIR COSTS 19____

DATE	ODOMETER READING	RECORD THE TYPE OF WORK PERFORMED ON YOUR CAR	TOTAL COST	
		ANNUAL REPAIR COST		

MAINTENANCE COSTS 19____

DATE	ODOMETER READING	RECORD THE TYPE OF WORK PERFORMED ON YOUR CAR	TOTAL COST	
		TIRES ROTATED (SPRING)		
		SPRING TUNE-UP AND OIL CHANGE		
		TIRES ROTATED (FALL)		
		FALL TUNE-UP AND OIL CHANGE		
		INSPECT BRAKES		
		INSPECT STEERING AND SUSPENSION		
		LUBRICATE CHASSIS		
		REPLACE COOLANT		
		CHECK FLUID LEVELS		
		ANNUAL MAINTENANCE COST		

REPAIR COSTS 19____

DATE	ODOMETER READING	RECORD THE TYPE OF WORK PERFORMED ON YOUR CAR	TOTAL COST	
		ANNUAL REPAIR COST		

MAINTENANCE COSTS 19____

DATE	ODOMETER READING	RECORD THE TYPE OF WORK PERFORMED ON YOUR CAR	TOTAL COST	
		TIRES ROTATED (SPRING)		
		SPRING TUNE-UP AND OIL CHANGE		
		TIRES ROTATED (FALL)		
		FALL TUNE-UP AND OIL CHANGE		
		INSPECT BRAKES		
		INSPECT STEERING AND SUSPENSION		
		LUBRICATE CHASSIS		
		REPLACE COOLANT		
		CHECK FLUID LEVELS		
		ANNUAL MAINTENANCE COST		

REPAIR COSTS 19____

DATE	ODOMETER READING	RECORD THE TYPE OF WORK PERFORMED ON YOUR CAR	TOTAL COST	
		ANNUAL REPAIR COST		

MAINTENANCE COSTS 19____

DATE	ODOMETER READING	RECORD THE TYPE OF WORK PERFORMED ON YOUR CAR	TOTAL COST	
		TIRES ROTATED (SPRING)		
		SPRING TUNE-UP AND OIL CHANGE		
		TIRES ROTATED (FALL)		
		FALL TUNE-UP AND OIL CHANGE		
		INSPECT BRAKES		
		INSPECT STEERING AND SUSPENSION		
		LUBRICATE CHASSIS		
		REPLACE COOLANT		
		CHECK FLUID LEVELS		
		ANNUAL MAINTENANCE COST		

REPAIR COSTS 19____

DATE	ODOMETER READING	RECORD THE TYPE OF WORK PERFORMED ON YOUR CAR	TOTAL COST	
		ANNUAL REPAIR COST		

MAINTENANCE COSTS 19____

DATE	ODOMETER READING	RECORD THE TYPE OF WORK PERFORMED ON YOUR CAR	TOTAL COST	
		TIRES ROTATED (SPRING)		
		SPRING TUNE-UP AND OIL CHANGE		
		TIRES ROTATED (FALL)		
		FALL TUNE-UP AND OIL CHANGE		
		INSPECT BRAKES		
		INSPECT STEERING AND SUSPENSION		
		LUBRICATE CHASSIS		
		REPLACE COOLANT		
		CHECK FLUID LEVELS		
		ANNUAL MAINTENANCE COST		

REPAIR COSTS 19____

DATE	ODOMETER READING	RECORD THE TYPE OF WORK PERFORMED ON YOUR CAR	TOTAL COST	
		ANNUAL REPAIR COST		

MAINTENANCE COSTS 19____

DATE	ODOMETER READING	RECORD THE TYPE OF WORK PERFORMED ON YOUR CAR	TOTAL COST	
		TIRES ROTATED (SPRING)		
		SPRING TUNE-UP AND OIL CHANGE		
		TIRES ROTATED (FALL)		
		FALL TUNE-UP AND OIL CHANGE		
		INSPECT BRAKES		
		INSPECT STEERING AND SUSPENSION		
		LUBRICATE CHASSIS		
		REPLACE COOLANT		
		CHECK FLUID LEVELS		
		ANNUAL MAINTENANCE COST		

REPAIR COSTS 19____

DATE	ODOMETER READING	RECORD THE TYPE OF WORK PERFORMED ON YOUR CAR	TOTAL COST	
		ANNUAL REPAIR COST		

MAINTENANCE COSTS 19____

DATE	ODOMETER READING	RECORD THE TYPE OF WORK PERFORMED ON YOUR CAR	TOTAL COST	
		TIRES ROTATED (SPRING)		
		SPRING TUNE-UP AND OIL CHANGE		
		TIRES ROTATED (FALL)		
		FALL TUNE-UP AND OIL CHANGE		
		INSPECT BRAKES		
		INSPECT STEERING AND SUSPENSION		
		LUBRICATE CHASSIS		
		REPLACE COOLANT		
		CHECK FLUID LEVELS		
		ANNUAL MAINTENANCE COST		

Maintenance Record

REPAIR COSTS 19____

DATE	ODOMETER READING	RECORD THE TYPE OF WORK PERFORMED ON YOUR CAR	TOTAL COST	
		ANNUAL REPAIR COST		

MAINTENANCE COSTS 19____

DATE	ODOMETER READING	RECORD THE TYPE OF WORK PERFORMED ON YOUR CAR	TOTAL COST	
		TIRES ROTATED (SPRING)		
		SPRING TUNE-UP AND OIL CHANGE		
		TIRES ROTATED (FALL)		
		FALL TUNE-UP AND OIL CHANGE		
		INSPECT BRAKES		
		INSPECT STEERING AND SUSPENSION		
		LUBRICATE CHASSIS		
		REPLACE COOLANT		
		CHECK FLUID LEVELS		
		ANNUAL MAINTENANCE COST		

REPAIR COSTS 19____

DATE	ODOMETER READING	RECORD THE TYPE OF WORK PERFORMED ON YOUR CAR	TOTAL COST	
		ANNUAL REPAIR COST		

MAINTENANCE COSTS 19____

DATE	ODOMETER READING	RECORD THE TYPE OF WORK PERFORMED ON YOUR CAR	TOTAL COST	
		TIRES ROTATED (SPRING)		
		SPRING TUNE-UP AND OIL CHANGE		
		TIRES ROTATED (FALL)		
		FALL TUNE-UP AND OIL CHANGE		
		INSPECT BRAKES		
		INSPECT STEERING AND SUSPENSION		
		LUBRICATE CHASSIS		
		REPLACE COOLANT		
		CHECK FLUID LEVELS		
		ANNUAL MAINTENANCE COST		

Accident Data Forms

Follow these eight steps

1. Record the details

Date: Time:

Location:

Town or city:

Your speed: Other vehicle's estimated speed:

2. Exchange information with the other driver

Other driver's name:

Address:

Telephone Home: Office:

Driver's license number:

Vehicle registered to:

Make, model, and year:

License plate number and year:

Insurance policy number: Expiry date:

Insurance company and agent:

5. Note damages to either vehicle

On the diagrams below, indicate the point of impact—and resulting damages—with an arrow.

Your vehicle

Motorcycle Car Van

Other vehicle

Motorcycle Car Van

6. Note the weather and road conditions

- ☐ Clear
- ☐ Rain
- ☐ Freezing rain
- ☐ Snow
- ☐ Fog
- ☐ Dry road
- ☐ Wet road
- ☐ Snow-covered road
- ☐ Icy road
- ☐ Unpaved road

8. Sketch the scene

Draw a sketch of the accident scene, indicating the names of streets; traffic signals or highway markings; and the position of all vehicles, pedestrians, and witnesses at the time of the accident.

3. Get names of witnesses

Name:

Address:

Telephone Home: Office:

Name:

Address:

Telephone Home: Office:

4. Find out if anyone was injured

Name:

Injuries:

Taken to:

Name:

Injuries:

Taken to:

7. Note the circumstances

You	Other driver	
☐	☐	Driving while intoxicated
☐	☐	Exceeded speed limit
☐	☐	Driving too slowly
☐	☐	Did not yield right-of-way

You	Other driver	
☐	☐	Followed too closely
☐	☐	Failed to signal
☐	☐	Disregarded traffic control

Other: ____________

◀ Indicate points of compass—N.E.S.W.

Follow these eight steps

1. Record the details

Date: Time:

Location:

Town or city:

Your speed: Other vehicle's estimated speed:

2. Exchange information with the other driver

Other driver's name:

Address:

Telephone Home: Office:

Driver's license number:

Vehicle registered to:

Make, model, and year:

License plate number and year:

Insurance policy number: Expiry date:

Insurance company and agent:

5. Note damages to either vehicle

On the diagrams below, indicate the point of impact—and resulting damages—with an arrow.

Your vehicle

Motorcycle Car Van

Other vehicle

Motorcycle Car Van

6. Note the weather and road conditions

- ☐ Clear
- ☐ Rain
- ☐ Freezing rain
- ☐ Snow
- ☐ Fog
- ☐ Dry road
- ☐ Wet road
- ☐ Snow-covered road
- ☐ Icy road
- ☐ Unpaved road

8. Sketch the scene

Draw a sketch of the accident scene, indicating the names of streets; traffic signals or highway markings; and the position of all vehicles, pedestrians, and witnesses at the time of the accident.

3. Get names of witnesses

Name:

Address:

Telephone Home: Office:

Name:

Address:

Telephone Home: Office:

4. Find out if anyone was injured

Name:

Injuries:

Taken to:

Name:

Injuries:

Taken to:

7. Note the circumstances

You	Other driver	
☐	☐	Driving while intoxicated
☐	☐	Exceeded speed limit
☐	☐	Driving too slowly
☐	☐	Did not yield right-of-way

You	Other driver	
☐	☐	Followed too closely
☐	☐	Failed to signal
☐	☐	Disregarded traffic control

Other:

◀ Indicate points of compass—N.E.S.W.

Follow these eight steps

1. Record the details

Date: Time:

Location:

Town or city:

Your speed: Other vehicle's estimated speed:

2. Exchange information with the other driver

Other driver's name:

Address:

Telephone Home: Office:

Driver's license number:

Vehicle registered to:

Make, model, and year:

License plate number and year:

Insurance policy number: Expiry date:

Insurance company and agent:

5. Note damages to either vehicle

On the diagrams below, indicate the point of impact—and resulting damages—with an arrow.

Your vehicle

Motorcycle Car Van

Other vehicle

Motorcycle Car Van

6. Note the weather and road conditions

- ☐ Clear
- ☐ Rain
- ☐ Freezing rain
- ☐ Snow
- ☐ Fog
- ☐ Dry road
- ☐ Wet road
- ☐ Snow-covered road
- ☐ Icy road
- ☐ Unpaved road

8. Sketch the scene

Draw a sketch of the accident scene, indicating the names of streets; traffic signals or highway markings; and the position of all vehicles, pedestrians, and witnesses at the time of the accident.

3. Get names of witnesses

Name:

Address:

Telephone Home: Office:

Name:

Address:

Telephone Home: Office:

4. Find out if anyone was injured

Name:

Injuries:

Taken to:

Name:

Injuries:

Taken to:

7. Note the circumstances

You	Other driver	
☐	☐	Driving while intoxicated
☐	☐	Exceeded speed limit
☐	☐	Driving too slowly
☐	☐	Did not yield right-of-way

You	Other driver	
☐	☐	Followed too closely
☐	☐	Failed to signal
☐	☐	Disregarded traffic control

Other:

◀ Indicate points of compass—N.E.S.W.

How far is it to...?

Distances are in kilometres, are calculated along major highways, and include ferry travel.

1 KM = 0.6 MI

To convert to miles, divide by 10 and multiply by 6.

	BANFF	BRANDON	CALGARY	CHARLOTTETOWN	CHICOUTIMI	DAWSON CREEK	EDMONTON	FLIN FLON	FREDERICTON	GASPÉ	HALIFAX	HAMILTON	JASPER	KENORA	MONCTON
ATLANTA	4207	2755	4078	2744	2562	4968	4377	3442	2397	2968	2666	1494	4493	2753	2569
BANFF	•	1259	129	5079	4348	1019	428	1362	4706	4823	5121	3631	286	1669	4904
BOSTON	4471	3212	4342	999	835	4954	4363	3899	652	1223	921	840	4731	2802	824
BRANDON	1259	•	1130	3864	3090	1741	1151	726	3447	3565	3862	2372	1519	410	3689
CALGARY	129	1130	•	4931	4220	890	299	1233	4558	4694	4973	3502	415	1540	4756
CHARLOTTETOWN	5079	3864	4931	•	935	5554	4963	4500	373	845	280	1854	5332	3402	175
CHICAGO	2905	1646	2776	2577	1846	3388	2797	2334	2203	2321	2618	784	3166	1236	2401
CLEVELAND	3467	2208	3338	2025	1410	3949	3359	2895	1677	1886	1986	418	3727	1798	1849
DALLAS	3462	2335	3333	4005	3333	4223	3632	3022	3658	4229	3927	2223	3748	2333	3830
DAWSON CREEK	1019	1741	890	5554	4831	•	591	1642	5189	5306	5684	4113	752	2152	5378
DENVER	2091	1959	1962	4231	3506	2852	2261	2646	3884	4455	4153	2396	2377	1957	4056
DETROIT	3367	2108	3238	2115	1384	3850	3259	2795	1741	1859	2157	322	3627	1698	1939
EDMONTON	428	1151	299	4963	4241	591	•	1051	4598	4715	5013	3523	369	1561	4788
FAIRBANKS	3495	4218	3367	8031	7308	2477	3067	4118	7665	7783	8081	6590	3228	4628	7885
FREDERICTON	4706	3447	4588	373	562	5189	4598	4134	•	700	415	1440	4966	3037	198
GASPÉ	4823	3565	4694	845	679	5306	4715	4252	700	•	945	1558	5084	3154	669
HALIFAX	5121	3862	4973	280	997	5604	5013	4550	415	945	•	1856	5382	3452	275
HAMILTON	3631	2372	3502	1854	1083	4113	3523	3059	1440	1558	1856	•	3891	1962	1630
INDIANAPOLIS	3217	1959	3088	2543	1846	3700	3109	2646	2195	2321	2504	787	3478	1548	2367
JASPER	286	1519	415	5332	4609	752	369	1419	4966	5084	5382	3891	•	1930	5156
LOS ANGELES	2723	3513	2707	6136	5406	3399	3006	3899	5763	5881	6178	4344	2874	3605	5961
MIAMI	5273	3821	5144	3489	3204	6034	5443	4508	3142	3713	3411	2467	5559	3819	3314
MINNEAPOLIS	2190	932	2062	3058	2335	2673	2082	1619	2692	2810	3108	1447	2451	708	2882
MONCTON	4904	3689	4756	175	760	5378	4788	4324	198	669	275	1630	5156	3227	•
MONTRÉAL	3872	2614	3743	1199	476	4355	3764	3301	834	951	1249	607	4133	2203	1024
NEW ORLEANS	4161	3005	4032	3614	3228	4922	4331	3692	3267	3838	3536	2115	4447	3003	3439
NEW YORK	4448	3190	4319	1353	1070	4931	4340	3877	1009	1540	1278	818	4709	2779	1181
NORTH BAY	3314	2055	3185	1757	1035	3796	3206	2742	1392	1510	1807	402	3574	1645	1582
OTTAWA	3682	2424	3553	1389	666	4165	3574	3111	1024	1141	1439	467	3943	3013	1213
PHILADELPHIA	4093	2834	3964	1506	1202	4575	3985	3521	1159	1672	1427	813	4353	2424	1331
PORT AUX BASQUES	5555	4297	5407	521	1411	6030	5440	4976	850	1321	576	2282	5808	3879	652
PRINCE GEORGE	632	1865	761	5678	4955	406	715	1765	5312	5430	5728	4237	346	2276	5502
QUÉBEC	4142	2884	4014	959	206	4625	4035	3571	586	703	982	877	4403	2474	784
REGINA	893	365	764	4178	3455	1376	785	752	3813	3930	4228	2737	1154	776	4002
RIVIÈRE-DU-LOUP	4324	3066	4196	755	180	4807	4216	3753	381	499	797	1059	4585	2655	579
ROCHESTER	3829	2570	3700	1625	1012	4311	3721	3257	1278	1487	1587	200	4089	2160	1450
SAINT JOHN	4812	3553	4664	323	649	5295	4704	4241	106	806	309	1547	5073	3143	148
ST. JOHN'S	6482	5224	6334	1448	2338	6957	6367	5903	1777	2248	1503	3209	6735	4806	1579
ST. LOUIS	3292	1840	3163	2911	2238	4053	3462	2527	2564	3135	2833	1128	3578	1838	2736
SAN FRANCISCO	2050	3090	2179	5181	5451	2717	2478	3476	5808	5926	6223	4389	2634	3634	6006
SASKATOON	748	623	620	4435	3713	1118	528	613	4070	4188	4485	2995	896	1033	4260
SAULT STE. MARIE	2887	1629	2758	2184	1461	3370	2779	2316	1819	1936	2234	744	3148	1218	2008
SEATTLE	1081	2340	1210	5811	5089	1318	1360	2411	5446	5564	5861	4027	1236	2750	5636
SHERBROOKE	4028	2770	3899	1151	420	4511	3920	3457	777	895	1193	763	4289	2359	975
SUMMERSIDE	5053	3795	4925	63	909	5528	4937	4474	348	819	317	1780	5306	3376	150
SYDNEY	5401	4142	5253	367	1257	5876	5285	4822	695	1167	422	2128	5654	3724	497
THUNDER BAY	2179	921	2050	2892	2169	2662	2071	1608	2527	2644	2942	1452	2440	510	2717
TORONTO	3563	2305	3434	1738	1015	4046	3455	2992	1373	1490	1788	68	3824	1894	1563
VANCOUVER	929	2187	1057	6000	5277	1202	1244	2290	5634	5752	6050	4559	875	2597	5824
VICTORIA	1033	2292	1162	6104	5382	1307	1349	2395	5739	5856	6154	4664	980	2702	5929
WASHINGTON	4105	2847	3977	1719	1384	4588	3998	3534	1371	1902	1640	832	4366	2437	1543
WHITEHORSE	2514	3236	2385	7049	6326	1495	2086	3137	6684	6801	7099	5609	2247	3647	6874
WINDSOR	3370	2111	3241	2111	1381	3853	3262	2799	1738	1856	2153	319	3631	1701	1936
WINNIPEG	1465	206	1336	3607	2884	1947	1357	893	3241	3359	3656	2166	1725	204	3431
YARMOUTH	4986	3727	4838	497	842	5449	4878	4414	280	980	345	1720	5246	3317	322

	MONTRÉAL	NIAGARA FALLS	OTTAWA	PORT AUX BASQUES	PRINCE ALBERT	PRINCE GEORGE	QUÉBEC	REGINA	RIVIÈRE-DU-LOUP	ROUYN	SAINT JOHN	ST. JOHN'S	SASKATOON	SAULT STE. MARIE	SHERBROOKE	SUMMERSIDE	SYDNEY	THUNDER BAY	TORONTO	VANCOUVER	VICTORIA	WHITEHORSE	WINDSOR	WINNIPEG	YARMOUTH
	2086	1425	1734	3221	3465	5691	2356	3100	2560	2188	2421	4148	3357	1674	2080	2719	3066	2341	1562	4894	4789	7591	1193	2549	2316
	3872	3700	3682	5555	912	632	4142	893	4324	3154	4812	6482	748	2887	4028	5053	5401	2179	3563	929	1033	2514	3370	1465	4986
	546	771	735	1476	3943	5077	629	3578	811	1189	676	2403	3835	1584	423	974	1321	2292	908	5399	5504	6396	1159	2953	571
	2614	2441	2424	4297	731	1865	2884	365	3066	1896	3553	5224	623	1629	2770	3795	4142	921	2305	2187	2292	3236	2111	206	3727
	3743	3571	3553	5407	784	761	4014	764	4196	3026	4664	6334	620	2758	3899	4925	5253	2050	3434	1057	1162	2385	3241	1336	4838
	1199	1860	1389	521	4543	5678	959	4178	755	1843	323	1448	4435	2184	1151	63	367	2892	1738	6000	6104	7049	2111	3607	497
	1370	853	1230	3053	2377	3512	1640	2012	1822	1444	2309	3980	2269	726	1520	2551	2898	1070	830	3833	3938	4883	465	1440	2483
	933	349	834	2501	2939	4073	1205	2573	1386	1112	1701	3428	2831	856	1090	1999	2346	1564	486	4395	4500	5444	282	2002	1637
	2857	2154	2581	4482	2849	4556	3127	2484	3331	2917	3682	5409	2741	2460	3064	3980	4327	2073	2291	3759	3654	6456	1922	2129	3577
	4355	4183	4165	6030	1193	406	4625	1376	4807	3637	5295	6957	1118	3370	4511	5528	5876	2662	4046	1202	1307	1495	3853	1947	5449
	3030	2327	3040	4708	2039	3254	3300	1674	3504	3090	3908	5635	1931	2363	3478	4206	4553	1962	2464	2457	2352	5154	2098	1753	3803
	908	391	768	2591	2839	3973	1178	2474	1360	995	1848	3518	2731	566	1064	2089	2437	1286	369	4295	4400	5345	3	1902	2021
	3764	3592	3574	5440	602	715	4035	785	4216	3046	4704	6367	528	2779	3920	4937	5285	2071	3455	1244	1349	2086	3262	1357	4878
	6832	6659	6642	8507	3669	2882	7102	3853	7284	6114	7772	9434	3595	5847	6988	8005	8352	5139	6523	3679	3784	982	6330	4424	7926
	834	1510	1024	850	4178	5312	586	3813	381	1477	106	1777	4070	1819	777	348	695	2527	1373	5634	5739	6684	1738	3241	280
	951	1627	1141	1321	4295	5430	703	3930	499	1595	806	2248	4188	1936	895	819	1167	2644	1490	5752	5856	6801	1856	3359	980
	1249	1925	1439	576	4593	5728	982	4228	797	1893	309	1503	4485	2234	1193	317	422	2942	1788	6050	6154	7099	2153	3656	345
	607	69	467	2282	3103	4237	877	2737	1059	694	1547	3209	2995	744	763	1780	2128	1452	68	4559	4664	5609	319	2166	1720
	1370	853	1230	3019	2689	3824	1640	2324	1822	1456	2219	3946	2581	978	1526	2517	2865	1382	830	4146	4250	5195	465	1753	2155
	4133	3961	3943	5808	970	346	4403	1154	4585	3415	5073	6735	896	3148	4289	5306	5654	2440	3824	875	980	2247	3631	1725	5246
	4929	4413	4789	5613	3513	2993	5200	3148	5382	5003	5869	7540	3405	4286	5086	6111	6458	3756	4390	2313	2211	4894	4025	3401	6043
	2728	2398	3054	3966	4530	6766	2998	4165	3202	3240	3166	4893	4422	2740	2812	3464	3811	3407	2535	5969	5864	8666	2248	3615	3061
	1859	1516	1669	3534	1662	2797	2129	1297	2311	1592	2799	4461	1555	874	2015	3032	3380	560	1493	2812	2710	4168	1128	726	2972
	1024	1699	1213	652	4368	5502	784	4002	579	1667	148	1579	4260	2008	975	150	497	2717	1563	5824	5929	6874	1936	3431	322
	•	676	190	1675	3344	4479	270	2979	452	644	940	2602	3236	985	156	1173	1521	1693	539	4801	4905	5850	904	2408	1114
	2752	2046	2874	4091	3515	5276	3022	3150	3226	2835	3291	5018	3407	2262	2836	3589	3936	2536	2183	4479	4374	7176	1843	2799	3186
	613	748	777	1833	3920	5055	864	3555	1041	1257	1033	2760	3813	1561	657	1331	1679	2269	885	5414	5518	6463	1136	2984	929
	558	472	369	2234	2786	3920	829	2420	1011	291	1498	3161	2678	426	715	1732	2079	1135	335	4242	4347	5279	700	1849	1672
	190	536	•	1865	3154	4289	460	2789	642	552	1130	2792	3046	795	346	1363	1711	1503	399	4611	4715	5660	764	2218	1304
	745	744	772	1983	3565	4699	961	3199	1143	1389	1183	2752	3457	1556	806	1481	1828	2264	880	5021	5126	6070	921	2623	1078
	1675	2351	1865	•	5020	6154	1436	4654	1231	2319	800	927	4912	2660	1627	584	154	3368	2214	6476	6581	7525	2588	4083	840
	4479	4307	4289	6154	1316	•	4749	1500	4931	3761	5419	7081	1242	3481	4635	5652	6000	2786	4170	797	901	1901	3977	2071	5592
	270	946	460	1436	3615	4749	•	3249	204	914	673	2363	3507	1255	214	933	1281	1963	809	5071	5176	6120	1175	2678	866
	2979	2807	2789	4654	365	1500	3249	•	3431	2261	3919	5581	257	1981	3135	4152	4500	1286	2670	1822	1926	2871	2477	571	4104
	452	1128	642	1231	3796	4931	204	3431	•	1096	488	2158	3689	1437	396	729	1077	2145	991	5253	5358	6302	1357	2860	661
	536	143	436	2102	3301	4435	806	2935	988	893	1302	3029	3193	941	692	1600	1947	1650	266	4757	4862	5807	517	2364	1238
	940	1616	1130	800	4284	5419	673	3919	488	1584	•	1727	4176	1925	864	298	645	2633	1479	5741	5845	6790	1844	3347	174
	2602	3278	2792	927	5947	7081	2363	5581	2158	3246	1727	•	5839	3587	2554	1511	1081	4295	3141	7403	7775	8452	3515	5010	1783
	1762	1059	1986	3388	2622	4764	2032	2257	2236	1822	2588	4315	2514	1361	2034	2886	3233	1450	1196	3967	3862	6664	830	1634	2483
	4974	4458	4834	6658	3050	2311	5245	2858	5427	5049	5914	7585	2886	4331	5131	6156	6503	3964	4435	1630	1529	4212	4070	3430	6088
	3236	3064	3046	4912	164	1242	3507	257	3689	2519	4176	5839	•	2239	3392	4410	4757	1543	2927	1677	1782	2614	2734	829	4350
	985	813	795	2660	2359	3481	1255	1981	1437	718	1925	3587	2239	•	1141	2158	2506	708	676	3803	3907	4852	581	1423	2099
	4612	4096	4472	6288	1962	912	4899	1975	5065	4199	5552	7215	1830	3454	4768	5786	6133	3261	4073	232	130	2813	3703	2546	5726
	156	832	346	1627	3500	4635	214	3135	396	800	864	2554	3392	1141	•	1125	1473	1849	695	4957	5061	6006	1061	2564	1057
	1173	1849	1363	584	4517	5652	933	4152	729	1817	298	1511	4410	2158	1125	•	430	2866	1709	5974	6078	7023	2086	3581	472
	1521	2197	1711	154	4865	6000	1281	4500	1077	2165	645	1081	4757	2506	1473	430	•	3214	2060	6322	6426	7371	2433	3928	702
	1693	1521	1503	3368	1651	2786	1963	1286	2145	975	2633	4295	1543	708	1849	2866	3214	•	1384	3108	3212	4157	1289	715	2807
	539	137	399	2214	3051	4170	809	2670	991	626	1479	3141	2927	676	695	1709	2060	1384	•	4492	4596	5528	369	2099	1653
	4801	4628	4611	6476	1841	797	5071	1822	5253	4083	5741	7403	1677	3803	4957	5974	6322	3108	4492	•	105	2697	4299	2232	5914
	4905	4733	4715	6581	1946	901	5176	1926	5358	4188	5845	7775	1782	3907	5061	6078	6426	3212	4596	105	•	2802	4403	2337	6019
	932	763	1014	2195	3578	4712	1178	3212	1360	1576	1395	3122	3454	1394	1048	1693	2041	2271	900	5034	5139	6083	1014	2641	1291
	5850	5678	5660	7525	2688	1901	6120	2871	6302	5132	6790	8452	2614	4852	6006	7023	7371	4157	5528	2697	2802	•	5348	3524	6964
	904	388	764	2588	2842	3977	1175	2477	1357	991	1844	3515	2734	581	1061	2086	2433	1289	369	4299	4403	5348	•	1905	2018
	2408	2235	2218	4083	937	2071	2678	571	2860	1690	3347	5010	829	1423	2564	3581	3928	715	2099	2232	2337	3524	1905	•	3521
	1114	1790	1304	840	4458	5592	866	4104	661	1757	174	1783	4350	2099	1057	472	702	2807	1653	5914	6019	6964	2018	3521	•

Metric Conversion Chart

Speed

0 km/h 20 40 60 80 100 120 140 160

0 mph 10 20 30 40 50 60 70 80 90 100

Conversion factors

IMPERIAL TO METRIC

To change	Into	Multiply by
cubic feet	cubic metres	0.028
cubic inches	cubic centimetres	16.39
cubic yards	cubic metres	0.76
degrees Fahrenheit	degrees Celsius	(°F−32)×1.8
feet	metres	0.30
gallons (imperial)	litres	4.54
gallons (U.S.)	litres	3.79
horsepower (SAE)	kilowatts	0.746
inches	millimetres	25.40
inches	centimetres	2.54
miles, miles per hour	kilometres, kilometres per hour	1.61
ounces	grams	28.35
pints (imperial)	litres	0.57
pounds	kilograms	0.45
pound-feet	newton metres	1.35
pounds per square inch	kilopascals	6.88
quarts (imperial)	litres	1.14
square feet	square metres	0.093
square inches	square centimetres	6.45
square yards	square metres	0.836
tons	tonnes	0.91
yards	metres	0.914

METRIC TO IMPERIAL

To change	Into	Multiply by
centimetres	inches	0.39
cubic centimetres	cubic inches	0.061
cubic metres	cubic feet	35.31
cubic metres	cubic yards	1.307
degrees Celsius	degrees Fahrenheit	(1.8×°C)+32
grams	ounces	0.035
kilograms	pounds	2.20
kilometres, kilometres per hour	miles, miles per hour	0.62
kilopascals	pounds per square inch	0.145
kilowatts	horsepower (SAE)	1.34
litres	imperial pints	1.75
litres	imperial quarts	0.88
litres	imperial gallons	0.22
litres	U.S. gallons	0.26
metres	feet	3.28
metres	yards	1.09
millimetres	inches	0.039
newton metres	pound-feet	0.74
square centimetres	square inches	0.155
square metres	square feet	10.76
square metres	square yards	1.195
tonnes	tons	1.10

METRIC ABBREVIATIONS

°C	degrees Celsius
cm	centimetre (=10mm)
cm^2	square centimetre
cm^3	cubic centimetre
g	gram (=1000 mg)
kg	kilogram (=1000 g)
km	kilometre (=1000 m)
km/h	kilometres per hour
kPa	kilopascal
kW	kilowatt
kW•h	kilowatt-hour
L	litre (=1000 mL)
L/100 km	litres per 100 kilometres
m	metre (=100 cm)
N•m	newton metre
m^2	square metre
m^3	cubic metre
mg	milligram
mL	millimetre
mm	millimetre
t	tonne (=1000 kg)

TEMPERATURE

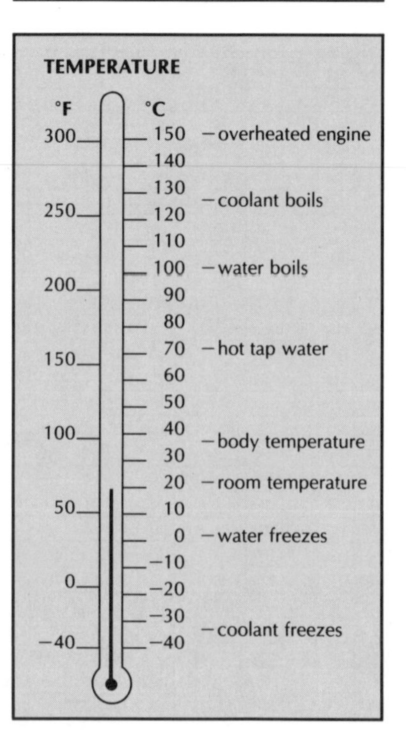